SAXOPHONE
ONE HUNDRED & ONE
SOLOS

Designed by Pearce Marchbank Studio
Cover photography by Rod Shone

ISBN 0.7119.0869.9
Order No. AM 62530

Exclusive Distributors:
Music Sales Limited
8/9 Frith Street, London W1V 5TZ, England.
Music Sales Pty. Limited
120 Rothschild Avenue, Rosebery, NSW 2018, Australia.

Music Sales complete catalogue lists thousands of
titles and is free from your local music book shop,
or direct from Music Sales Limited.
Please send a cheque/postal order for £1.50 for postage to
Music Sales Limited, 8/9 Frith Street, London W1V 5TZ.

Printed and bound in Great Britain by
J.B. Offset Printers (Marks Tey) Limited, Marks Tey, Essex

Wise Publications
London/New York/Sydney

AMERICAN PATROL

By: F. W. Meacham

ANGEL EYES

Words: Earl Brent
Music: Matt Dennis

AND I LOVE HER

Words and Music: John Lennon and Paul McCartney

A GARDEN IN THE RAIN

Words: James Dyrenforth
Music: Carroll Gibbons

BABY WON'T YOU PLEASE COME HOME

Words and Music: Charles Warfield and Clarence Williams

BIG NOISE FROM WINNETKA

Words: Gil Rodin and Bob Crosby
Music: Bob Haggart and Ray Baudac

CAN'T SMILE WITHOUT YOU

Words and Music: Chris Arnold, David Martin and Geoff Morrow

CUTE

Words: Stanley Styne
Music: Neal Hefti

DANCIN' IN THE KEY OF LIFE

Words and Music: Steve Arrington and India Arrington

DREAMING

Words and Music: Bud Flanagan and Reg Connelly

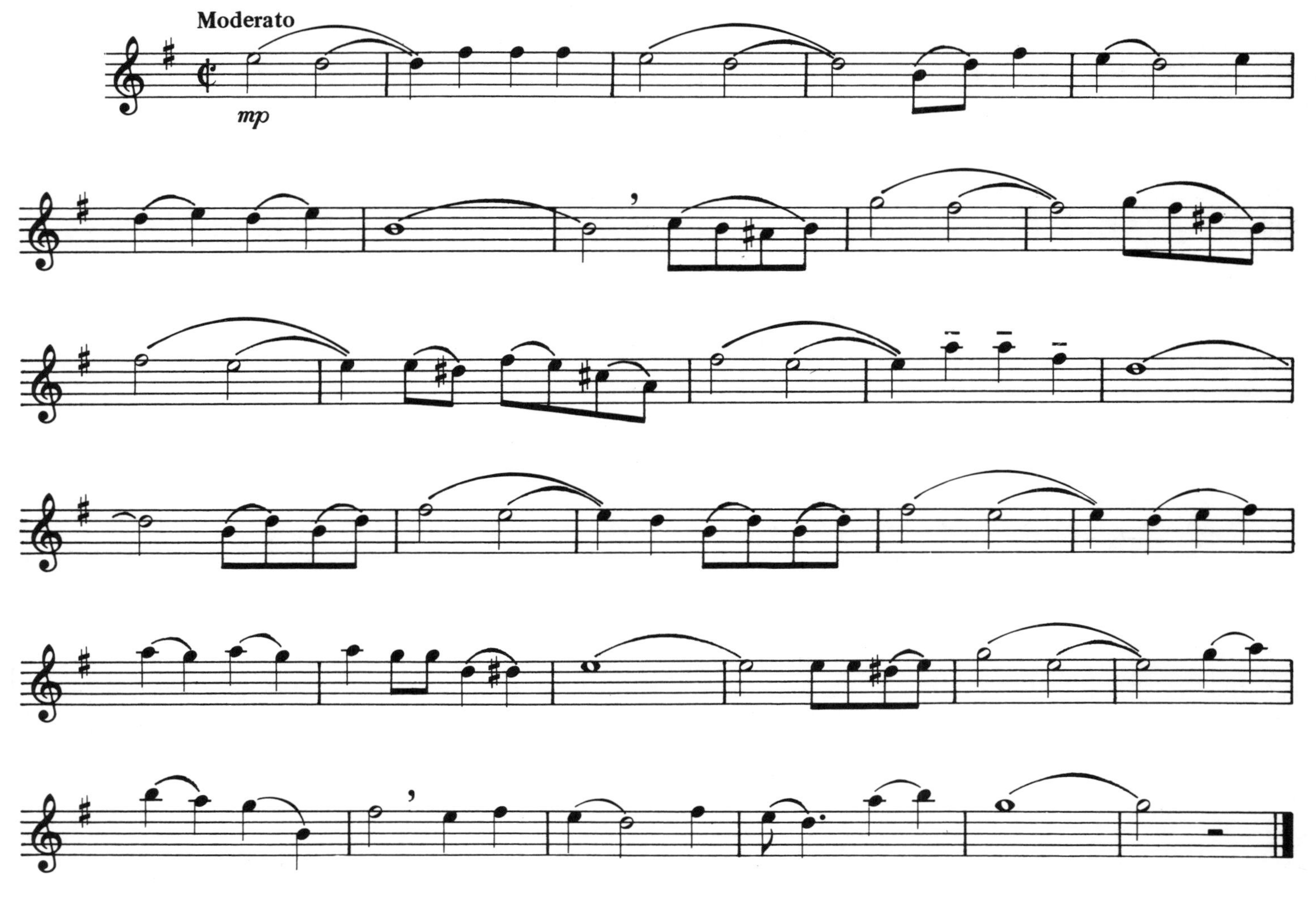

EASTENDERS (Theme from)

By: Leslie Osborne and Simon May

ELEANOR RIGBY

Words and Music: John Lennon and Paul McCartney

BE MY GIRL/SALLY

Words and Music: Sting and Andy Summers

BY THE FIRESIDE

Words and Music: Ray Noble, Jimmy Campbell and Reg Connelly

BUGLE CALL RAG

Words and Music: Jack Pettis, Billy Meyers and Elmer Schoebel

EVERY BREATH YOU TAKE

Words and Music: Sting

FAREWELL BLUES

Words and Music: Elmer Schoebel, Paul Mares and Leon Rappolo

Moderately

f

Mysterioso

FOR LENA AND LENNY

By: Quincy Jones

GO AWAY BLUES

Words and Music: Duke Ellington

FROM A WINDOW

Words and Music: John Lennon and Paul McCartney

GEORGIA ON MY MIND

Words: Stuart Gorrell

Music: Hoagy Carmichael

To Coda
D.%. al Coda
CODA

GREEN ONIONS

Music: Booker T. Jones, Steve Cropper, Al Jackson Jr. and Lewie Steinberg

THE HAWK TALKS

By: Louis Bellson

HEARTACHES

Words: John Klenner
Music: Al Hoffman

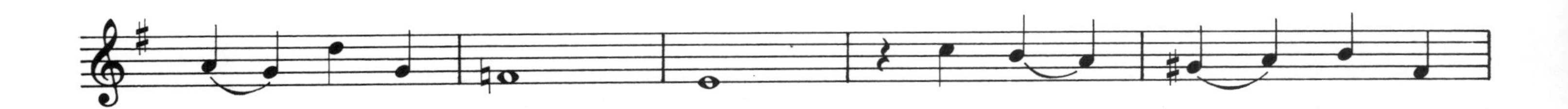

I AIN'T GOT NOBODY
(and there's nobody cares for me)

Words and Music: Roger Graham and Spencer Williams

HEY! BA-BA-RE-BOP

Words and Music: Lionel Hampton and Curley Hammer

HOME SWEET HOME

Traditional

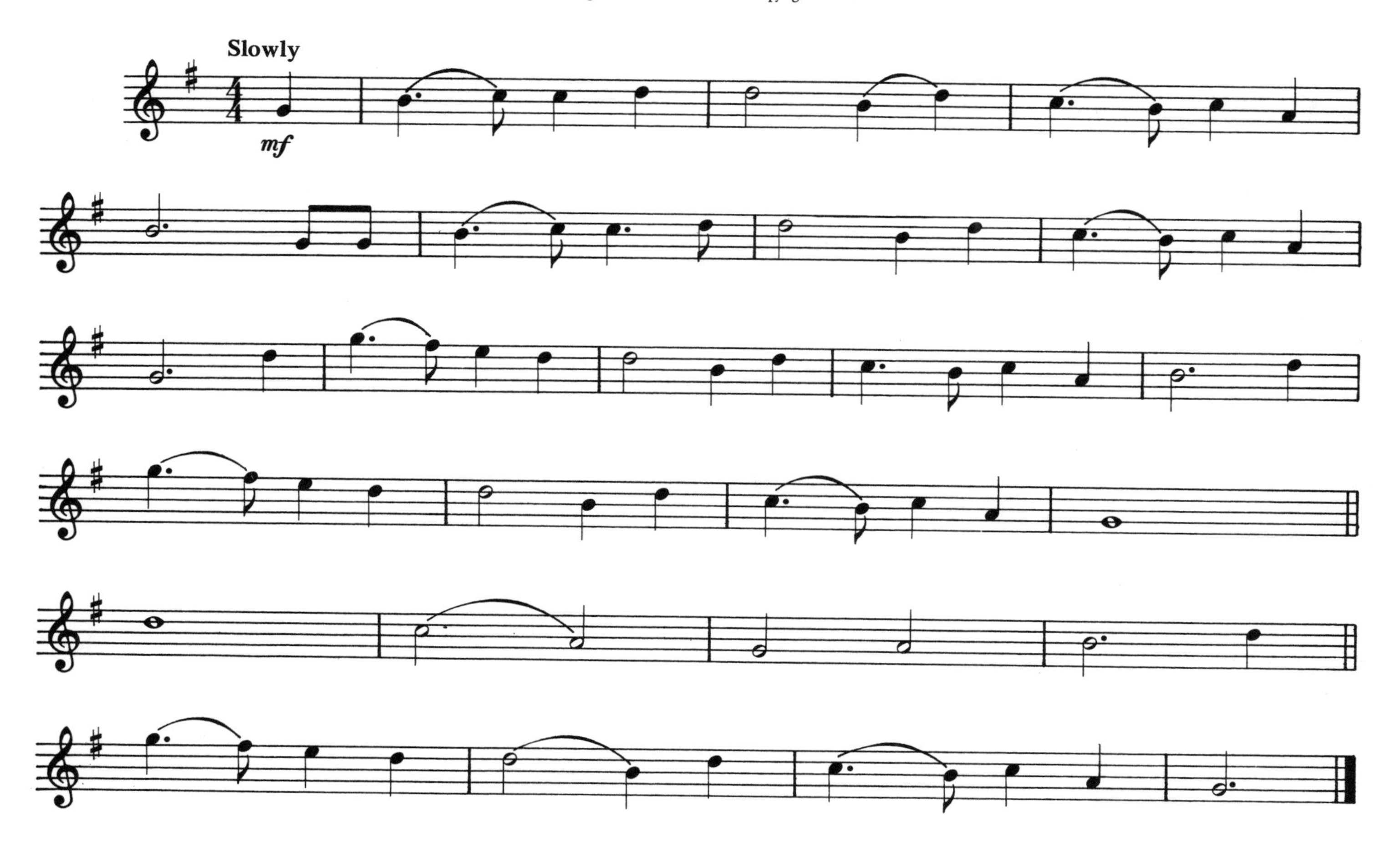

IF I HAD YOU

Words and Music: Ted Shapiro, Jimmy Campbell and Reg Connelly

IF YOU LOVE SOMEBODY SET THEM FREE

Words and Music: Sting

HOWARDS' WAY (Theme From)

By: Leslie Osborne and Simon May

HOLIDAY

Words and Music: Curtis Hudson and Lisa Stevens

I'M BEGINNING TO SEE THE LIGHT

Words and Music: Harry James, Duke Ellington, Johnny Hodges and Don George

I'LL REMEMBER APRIL

Words and Music: Don Raye, Gene de Paul and Patricia Johnson

T'AINT WHAT YOU DO (It's The Way That Cha Do It)

Words and Music: Sy Oliver and James Young

IN A SENTIMENTAL MOOD

Words and Music: Duke Ellington, Irving Mills and Manny Kurtz

IS YOU IS, OR IS YOU AIN'T (Ma' Baby)

Words and Music: Billy Austin and Louis Jordan

IT DON'T MEAN A THING
(If It Ain't Got That Swing)

Words: Irving Mills
Music: Duke Ellington

JUST THE TWO OF US

Words and Music: Ralph MacDonald, William Salter and Bill Withers

THE JOINT IS JUMPIN'

Words: Andy Razaf and J. C. Johnson
Music: Thomas Waller

IT'S A RAGGY WALTZ

Music: Dave Brubeck

LADY MADONNA

Words and Music: John Lennon and Paul McCartney

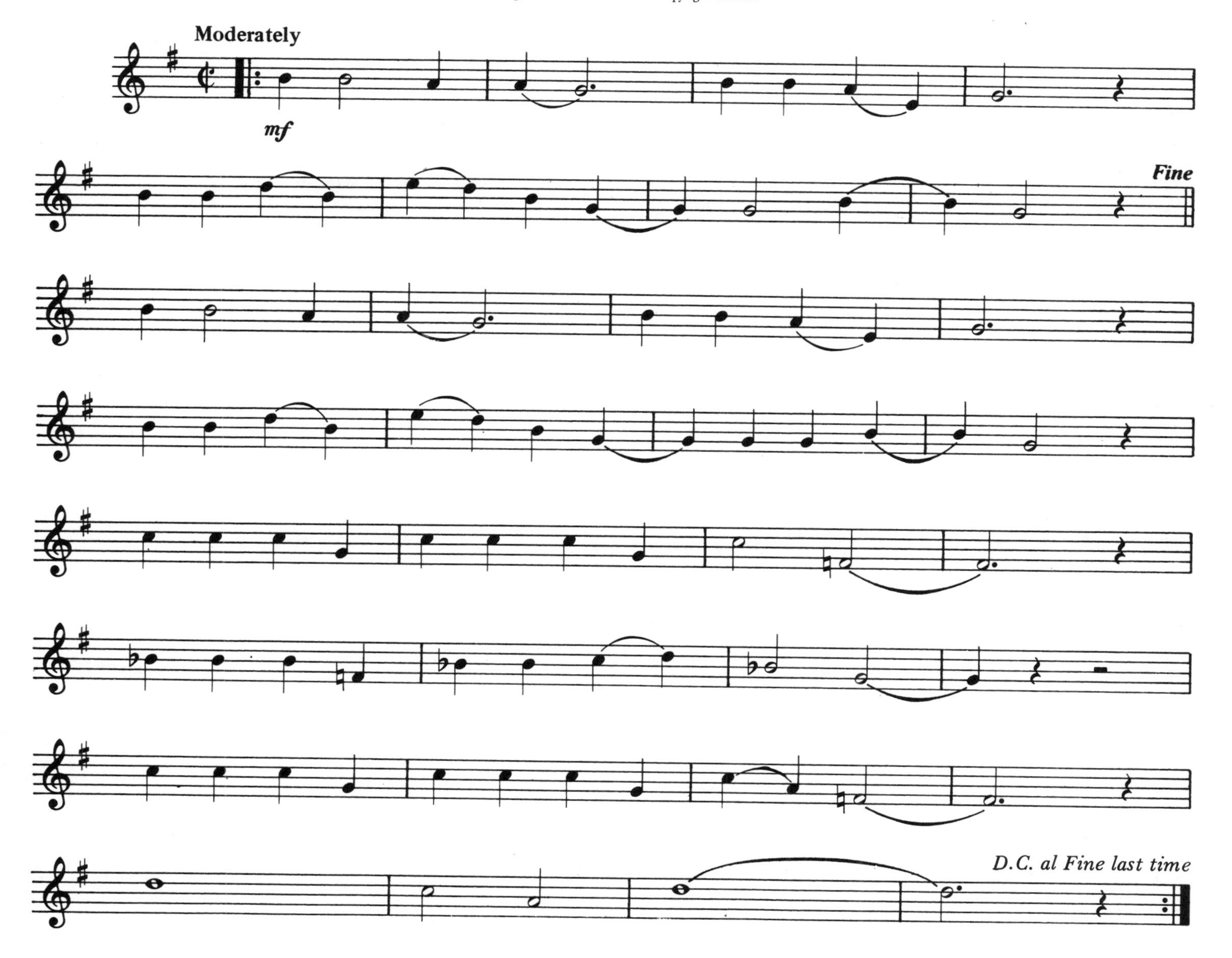

LEAN BABY

Words: Roy Alfred
Music: Billy May

LOVER MAN (Oh Where Can You Be)

Words and Music: Jimmy Davis, Roger Ram Ramirez and Jimmy Sherman

THE LINCOLNSHIRE POACHER

Traditional

THE LONESOME ROAD

Words: Gene Austin
Music: Nathaniel Shilkret

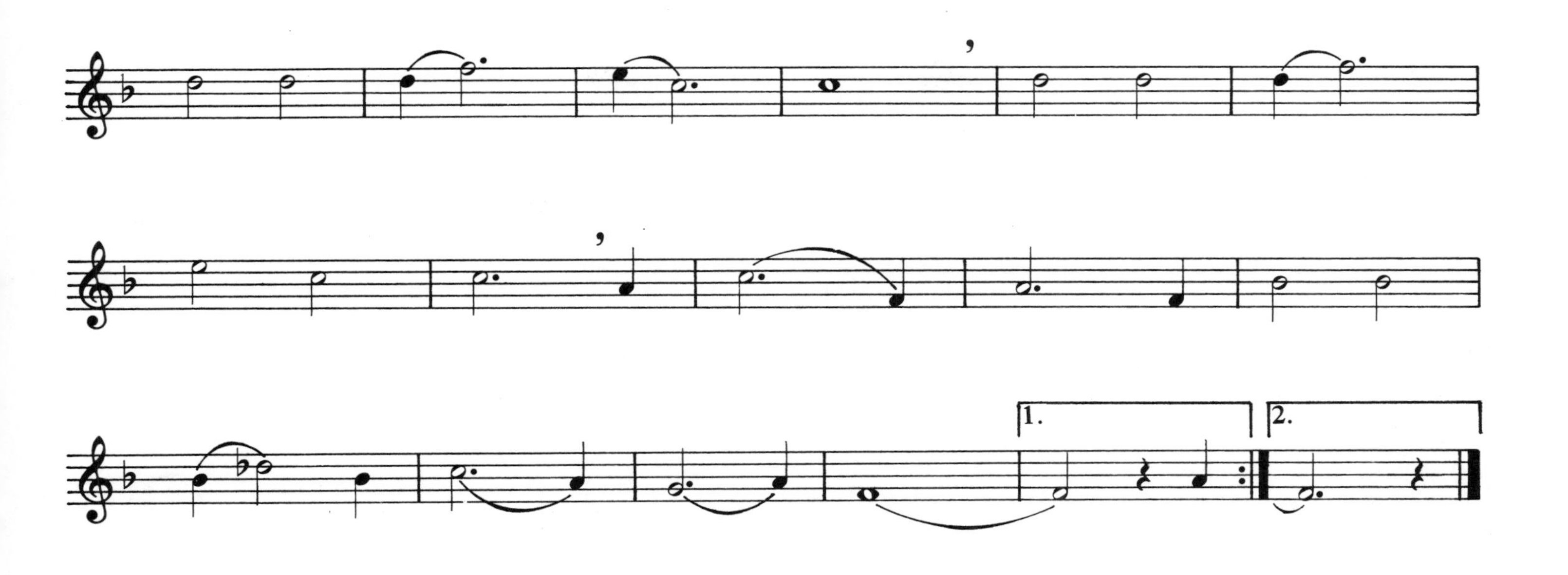

LARGO (From "The New World")

By: Antonin Dvořák

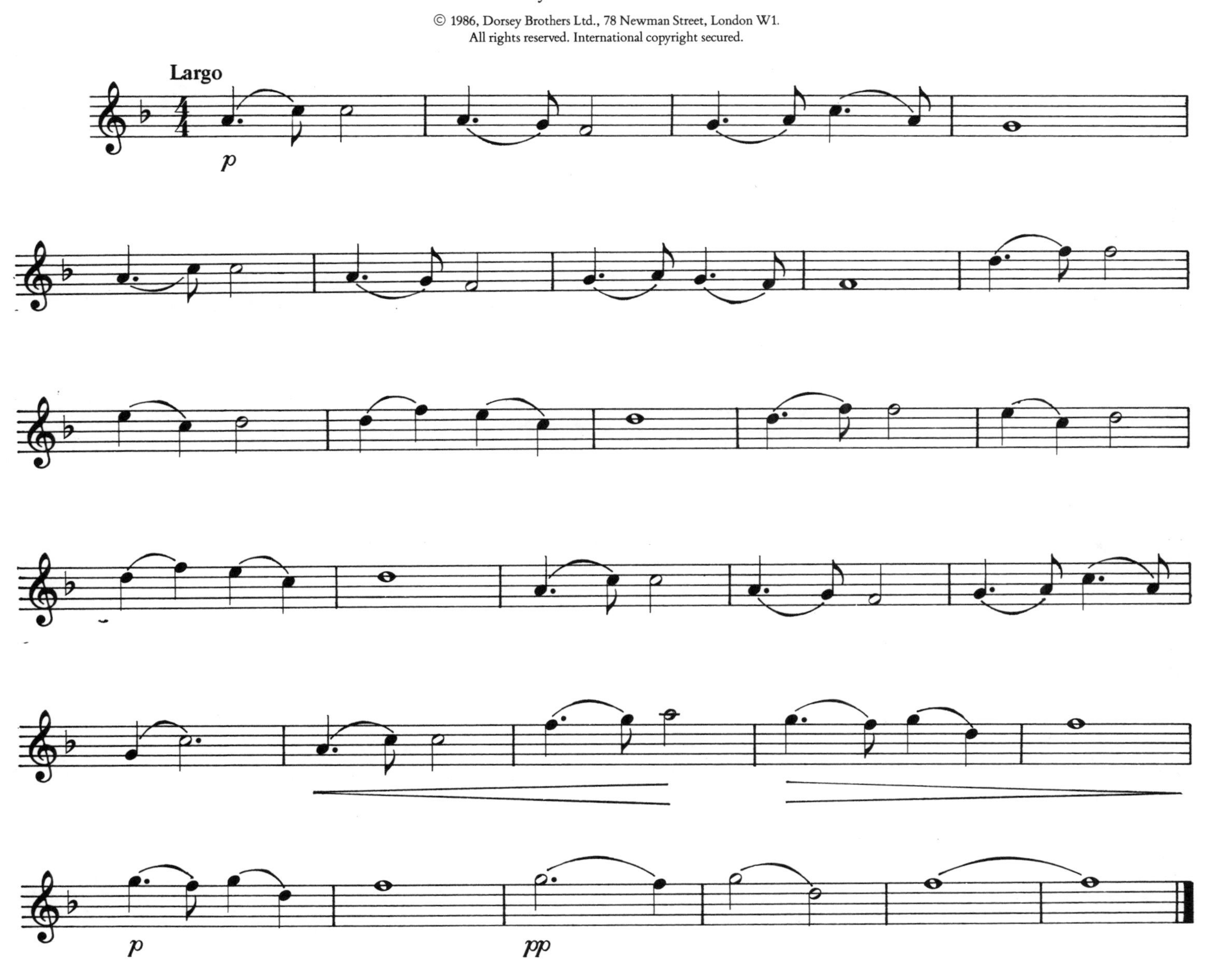

LUCILLE

Words and Music: Roger Bowling and Hal Bynum

MAMA DON'T ALLOW IT

Words and Music: Chas 'Cow Cow' Davenport

MASOKO TANGA

Words and Music: Sting

MISSISSIPPI MUD

Words and Music: Harry Barris

MELODY IN 'F'

By: Anton Rubinstein

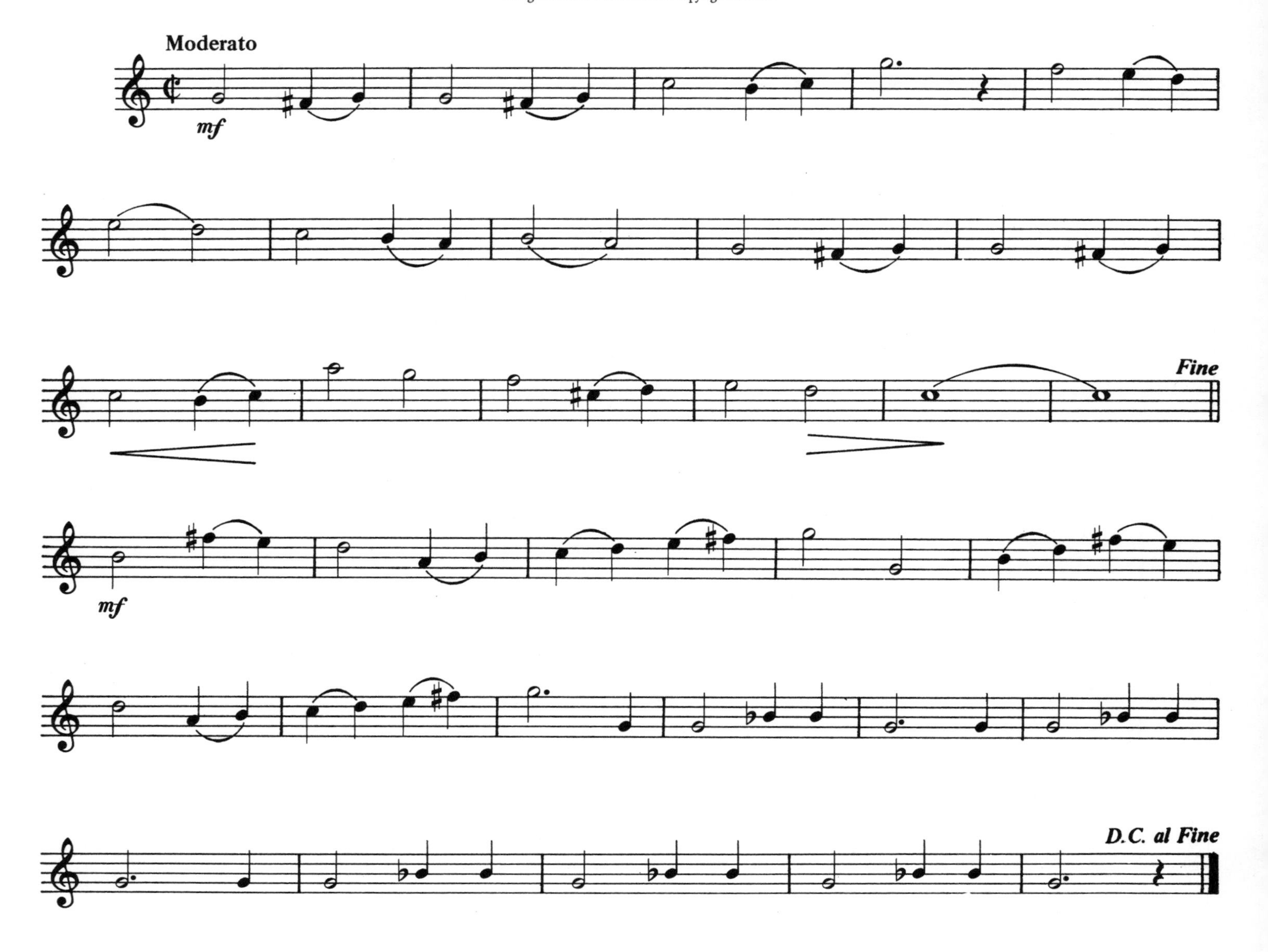

MEMPHIS BLUES

Words and Music: W. C. Handy

mf

MIDNIGHT IN MOSCOW

Based on a song by Vassili Soloviev and M. Matusovosky
New musical arrangement by Kenny Ball

NOCTURNE (from "A Midsummer Night's Dream")

By: Felix Mendelssohn

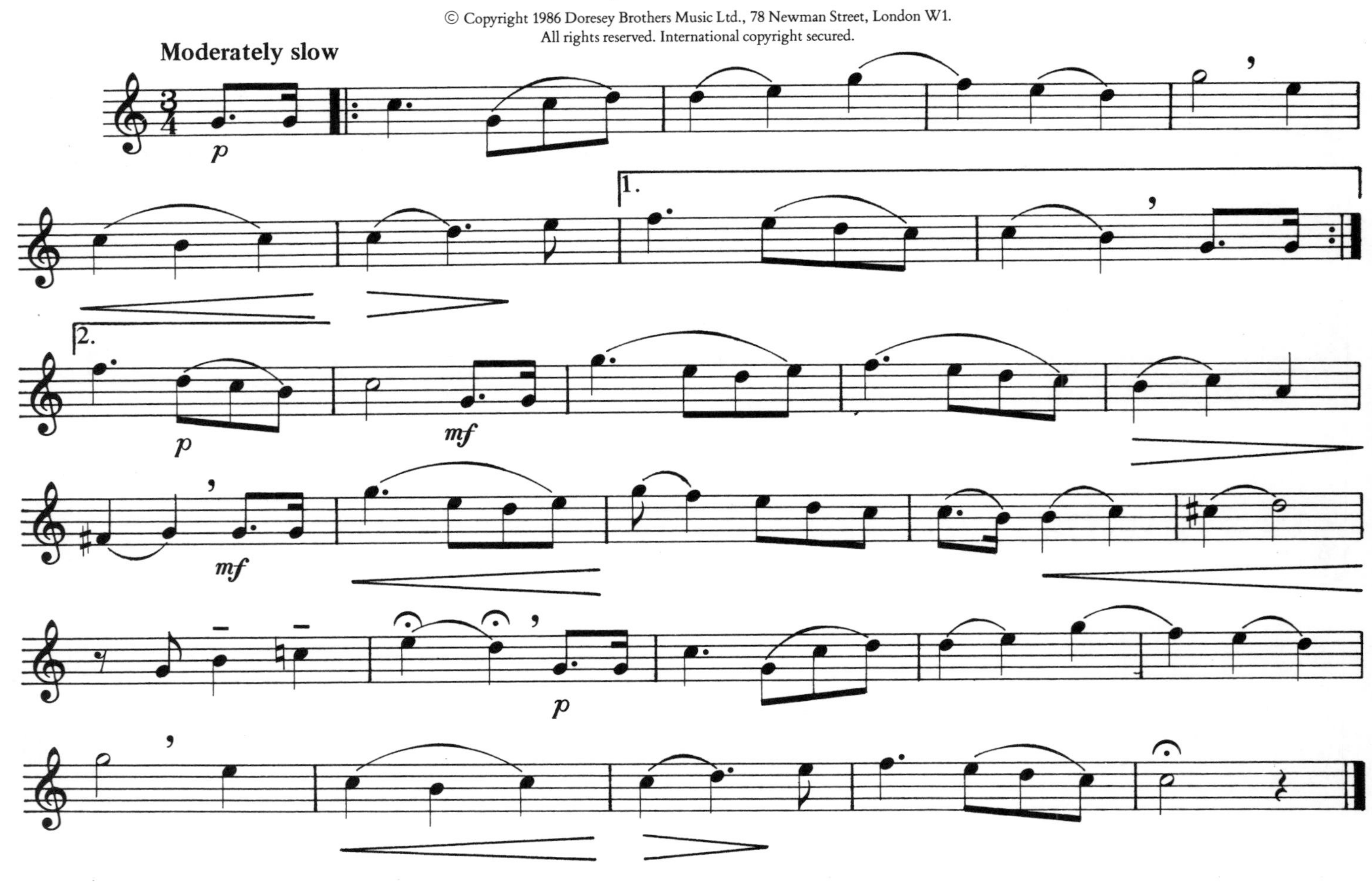

MOANIN'

Words: Jon Hendricks
Music: Bobby Timmons

MONEY FOR NOTHING

Words and Music: Mark Knopfler and Sting

MOOD INDIGO

Words and Music: Duke Ellington, Irving Mills and Albany Bigard

THE NIGHT WE CALLED IT A DAY

Words: Tom Adair
Music: Matt Dennis

NIGHT BOAT

Words and Music: Duran Duran

NIGHT TRAIN

Words: Oscar Washington and Lewis C. Simpkins
Music: Jimmy Forrest

OH, DIDN'T HE RAMBLE

Words and Music: Will Handy

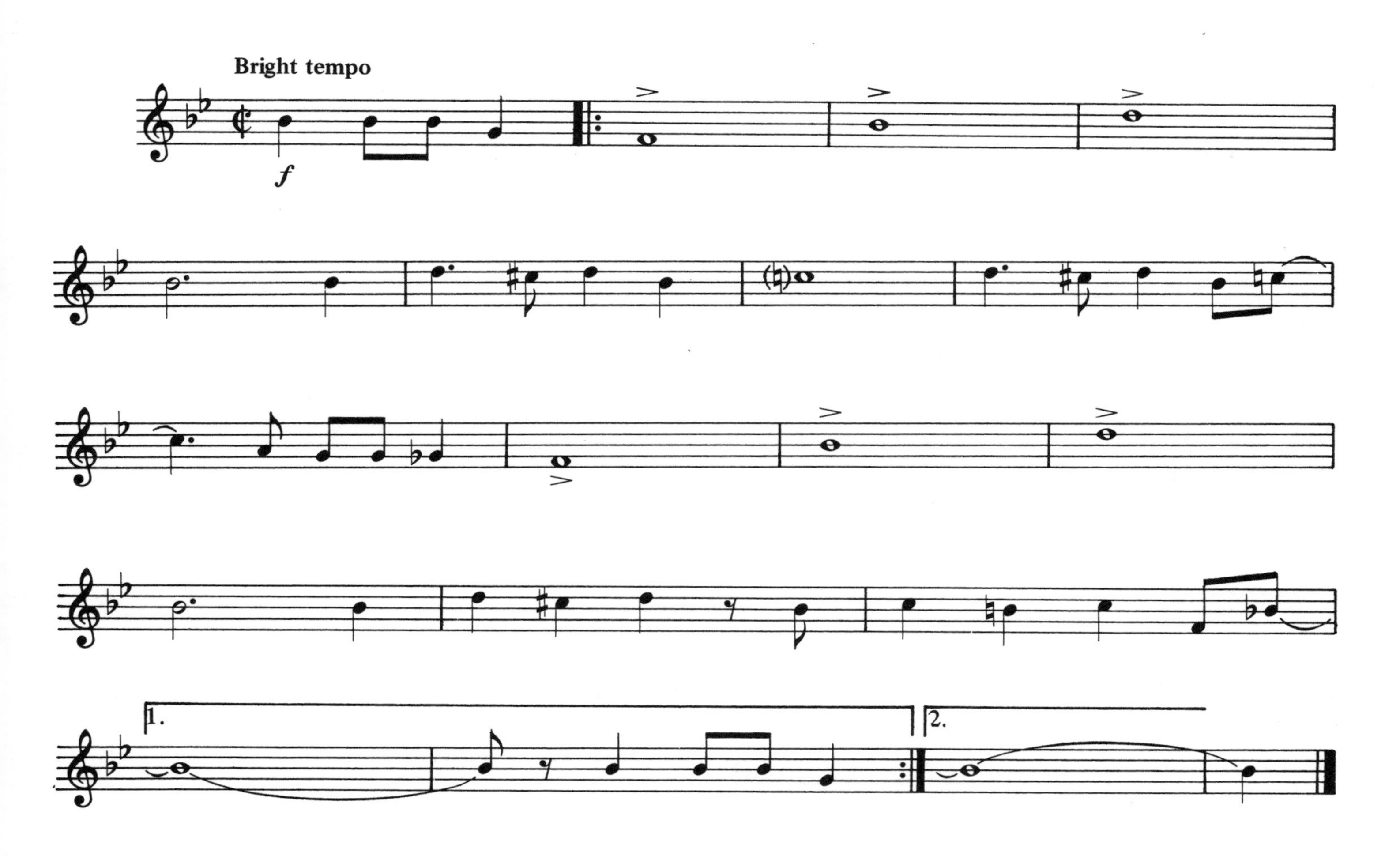

OH DEAR, WHAT CAN THE MATTER BE?

Traditional

OH LOOK AT ME NOW

Words: John DeVries
Music: Joe Bushkin

OLIVER

Words and Music: Lionel Bart

O SOLDIER WON'T YOU MARRY ME?

Traditional

OL' MAN MOSE

By: Louis Armstrong and Zilner Trenton Randolph

ON THE CREST OF A WAVE

Words and Music: Ralph Reader

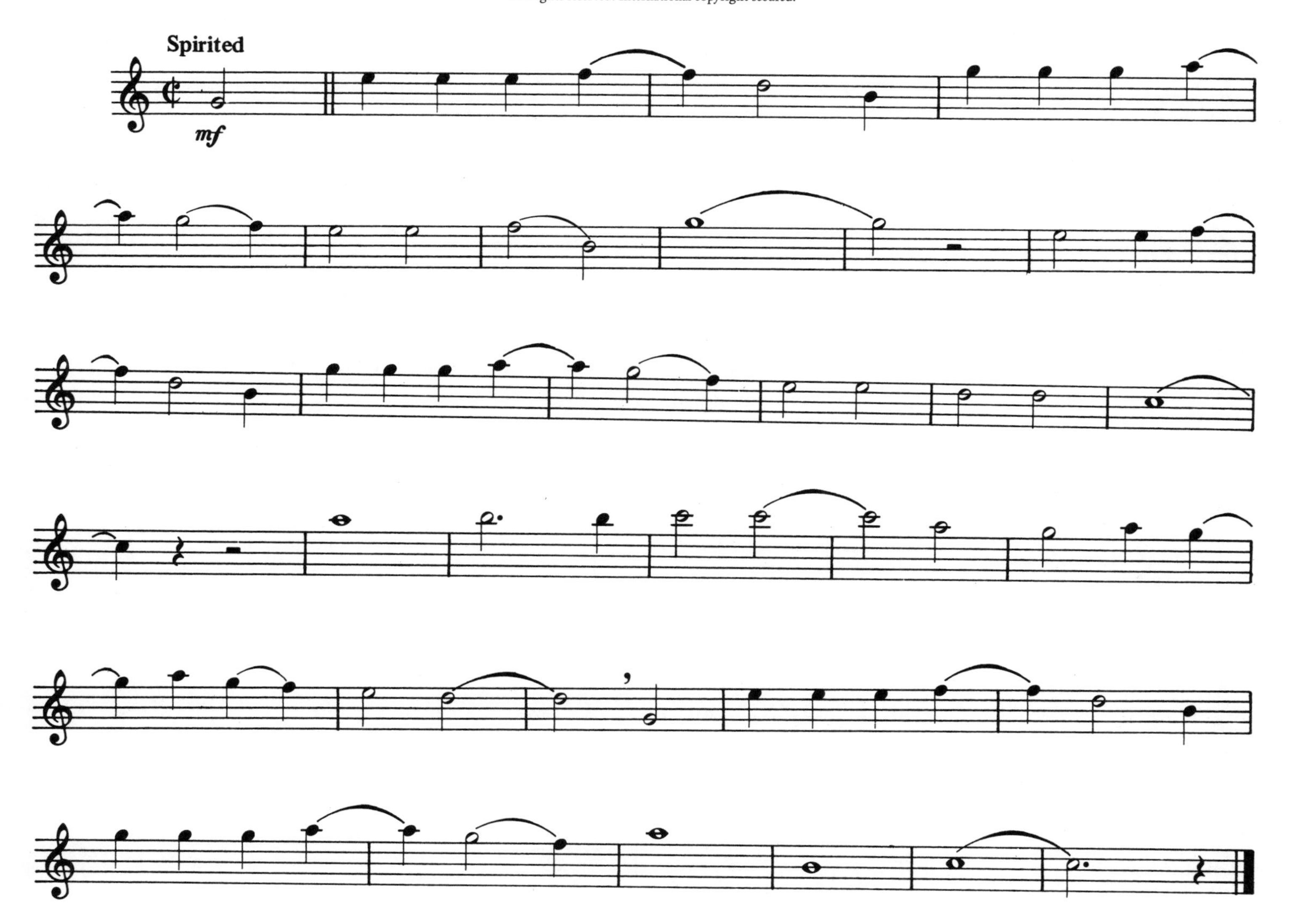

PASSION FLOWER

By: Billy Strayhorn

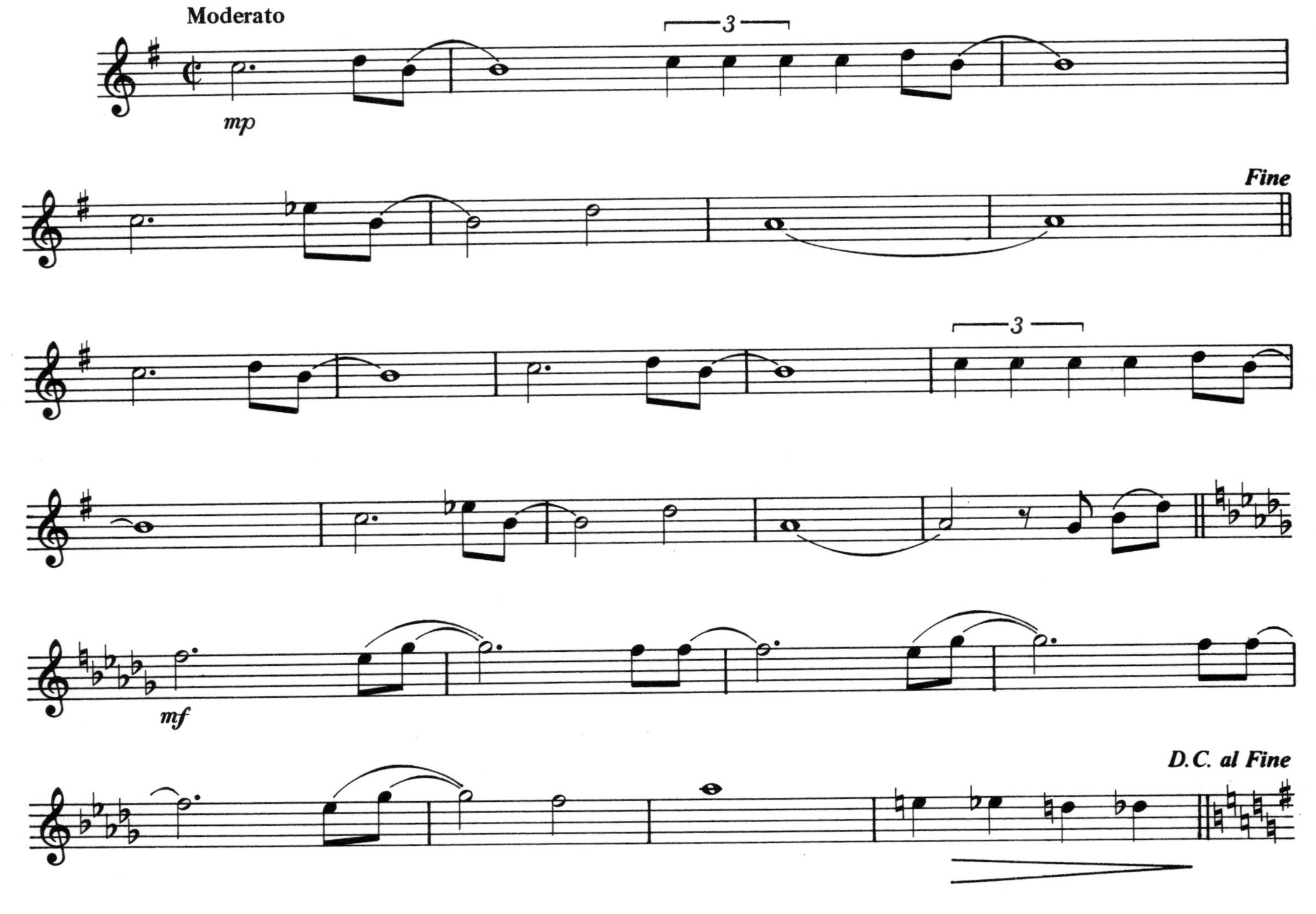

PETITE FLEUR (Litte Flower)

Words and Music: Sydney Bechet

mf
mp
mf
mp

THE POWER OF LOVE

Words and Music: C. de Rouge, G. Mende, J. Rush and S. Applegate

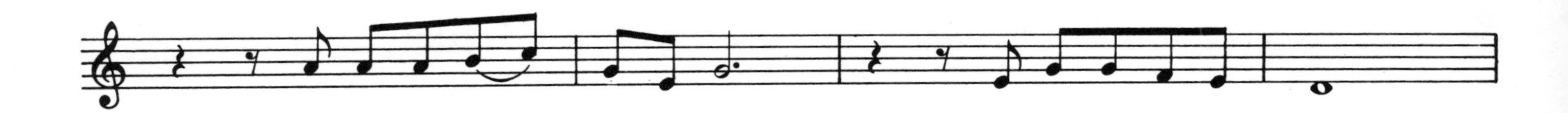

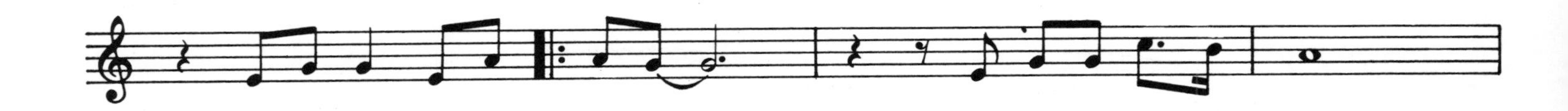

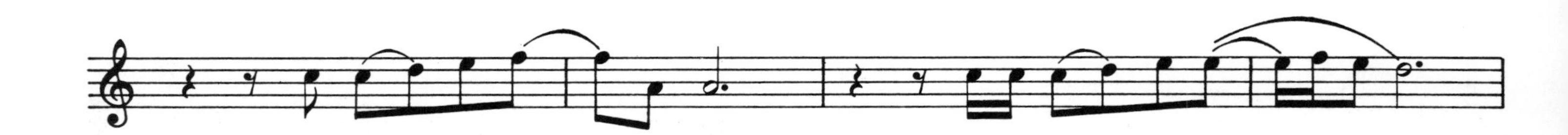

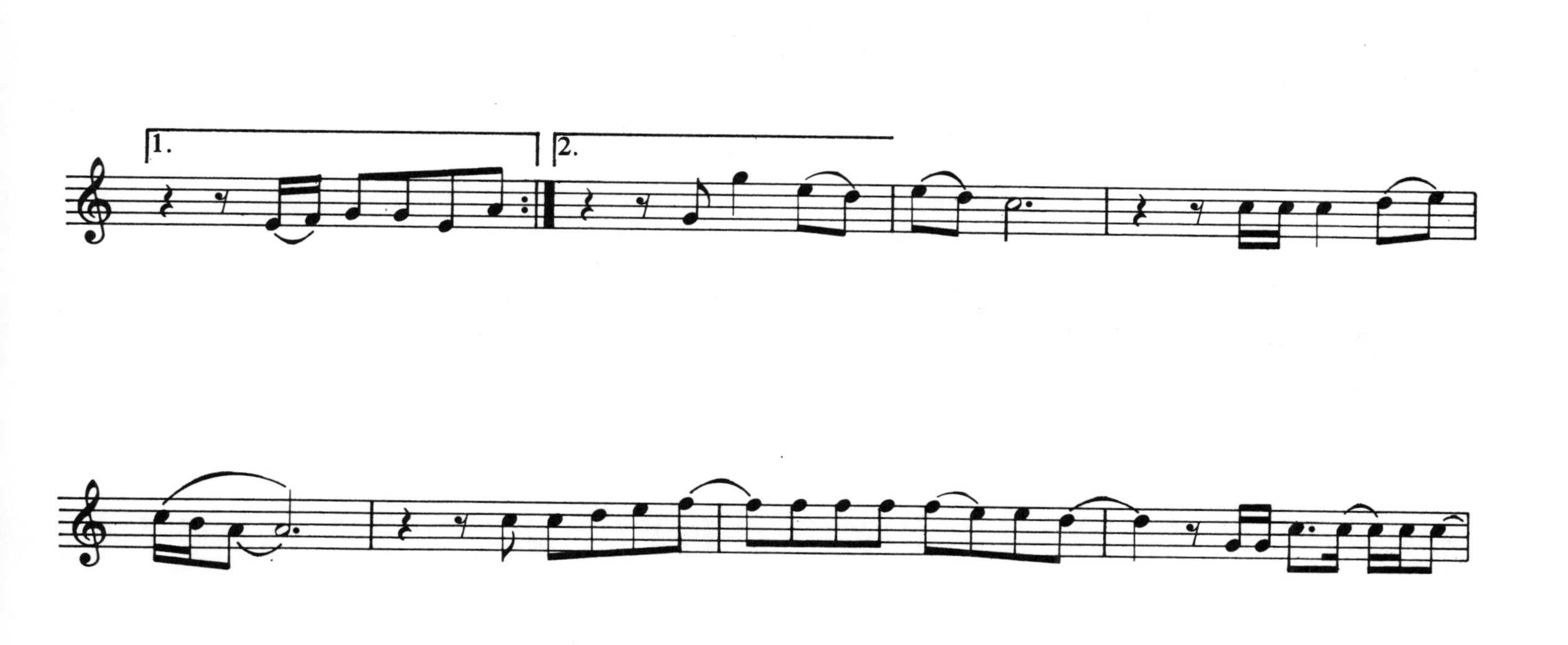
1.
2.

To Coda

D.%. al Coda
CODA

1.
2.

PLANET EARTH

Words and Music: Duran Duran

QUEEN OF HEARTS

Traditional

RAINCHECK

By: Billy Strayhorn

SHORT STOP

By: Shorty Rogers

SEVEN ELEVEN

By: Carpenter and Williams

SATIN DOLL

Words: Johnny Mercer
Music: Duke Ellington and Billy Strayhorn

THE SEVENTH STRANGER

Words and Music: Duran Duran

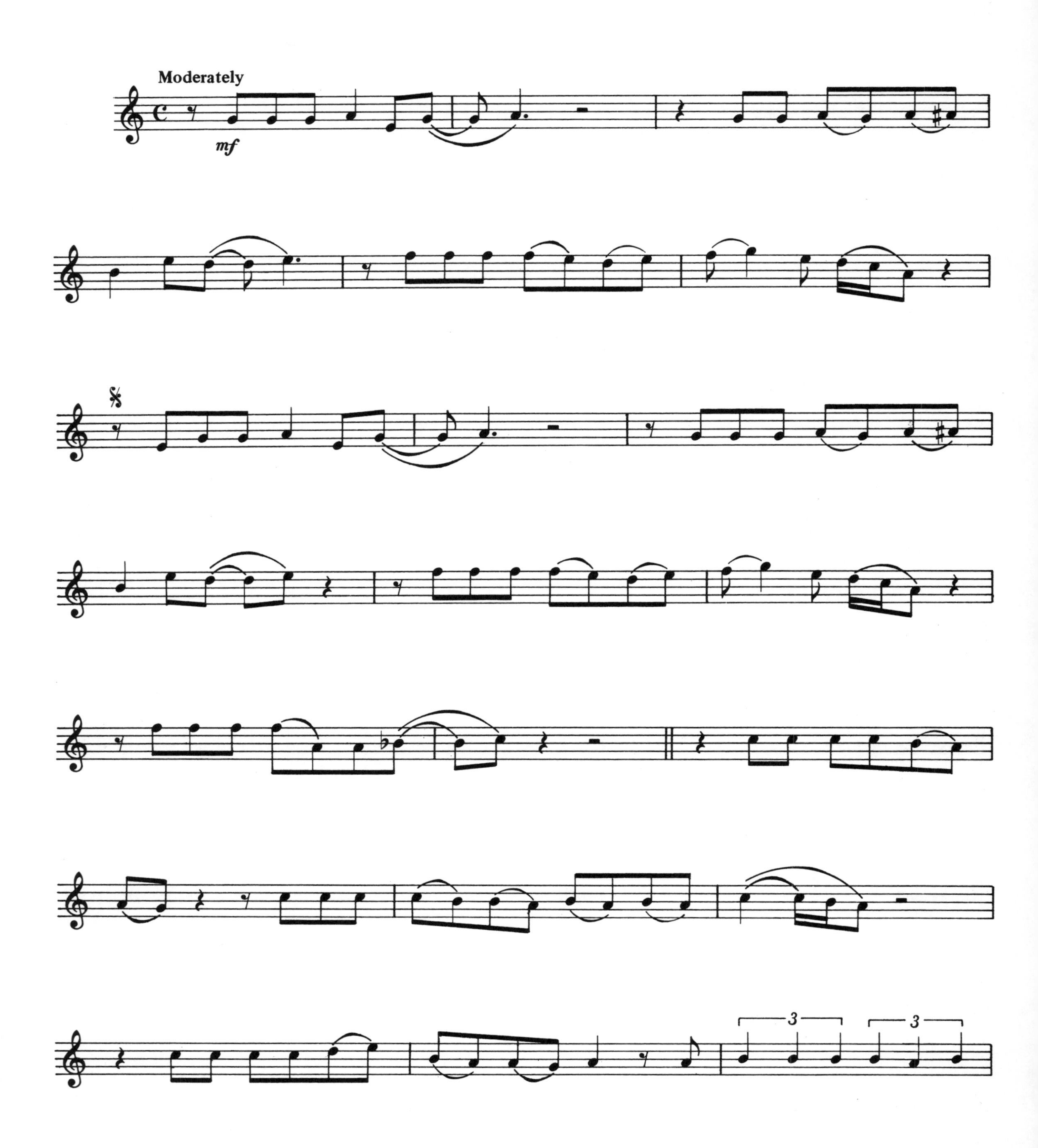

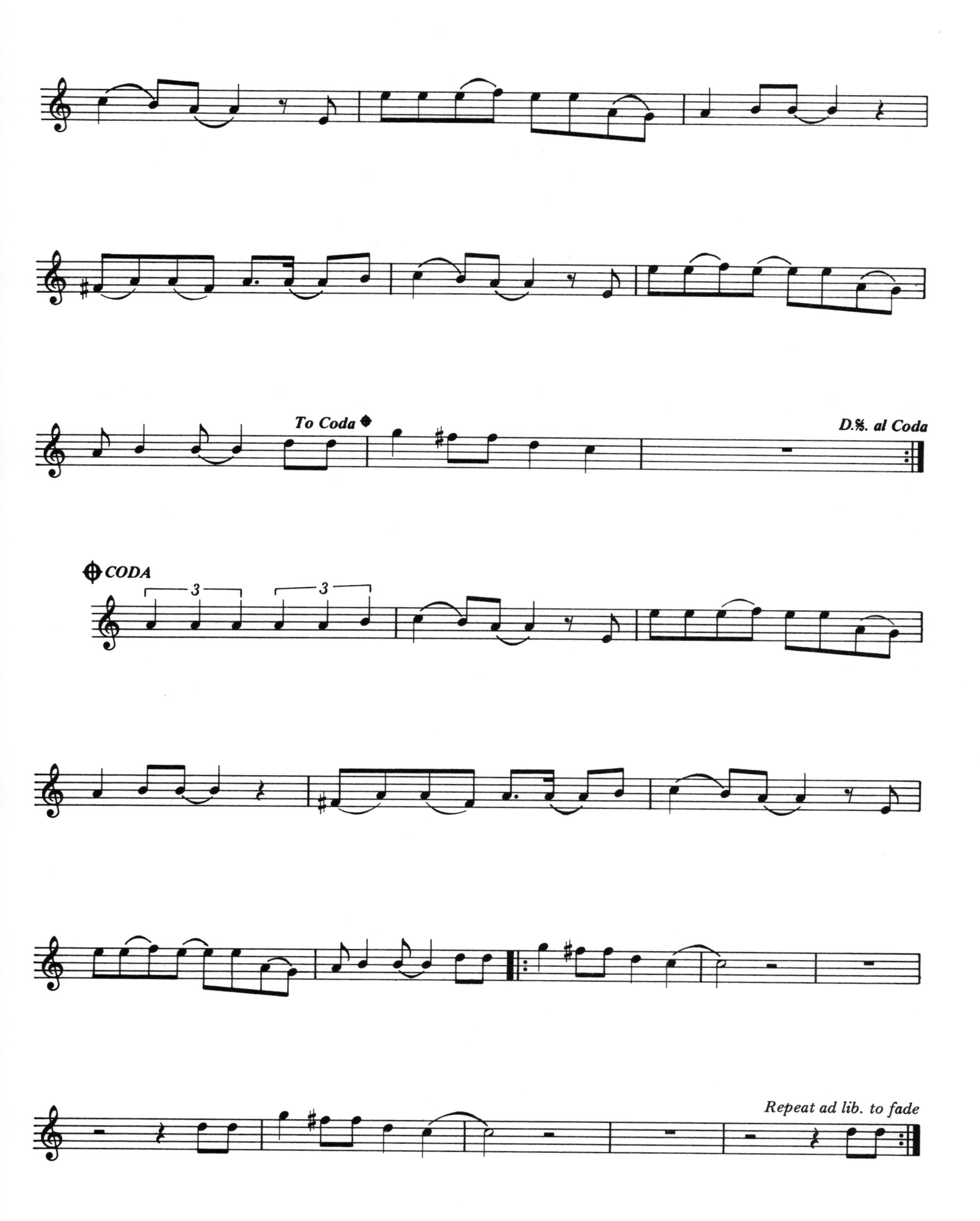
To Coda
D.%. al Coda
CODA
3
3
Repeat ad lib. to fade

STOMP, LOOK AND LISTEN

By: Duke Ellington

SOLITUDE

Words: Eddie de Lange and Irving Mills
Music: Duke Ellington

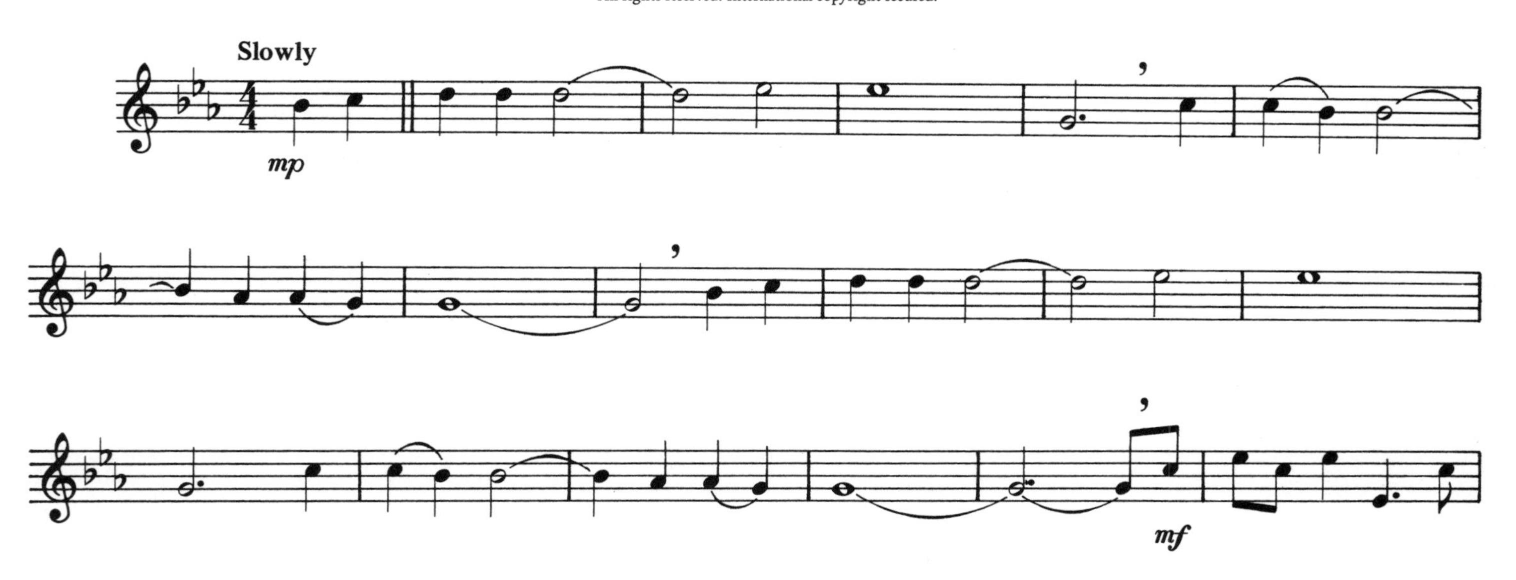

SOLVEIG'S SONG (from "Peer Gynt")

By: Edvard Grieg

SOMETHING

Words and Music: George Harrison

STRUTTIN' WITH SOME BARBECUE

Words: Don Raye
Music: Louis Armstrong

ST. THOMAS

By: Sonny Rollins

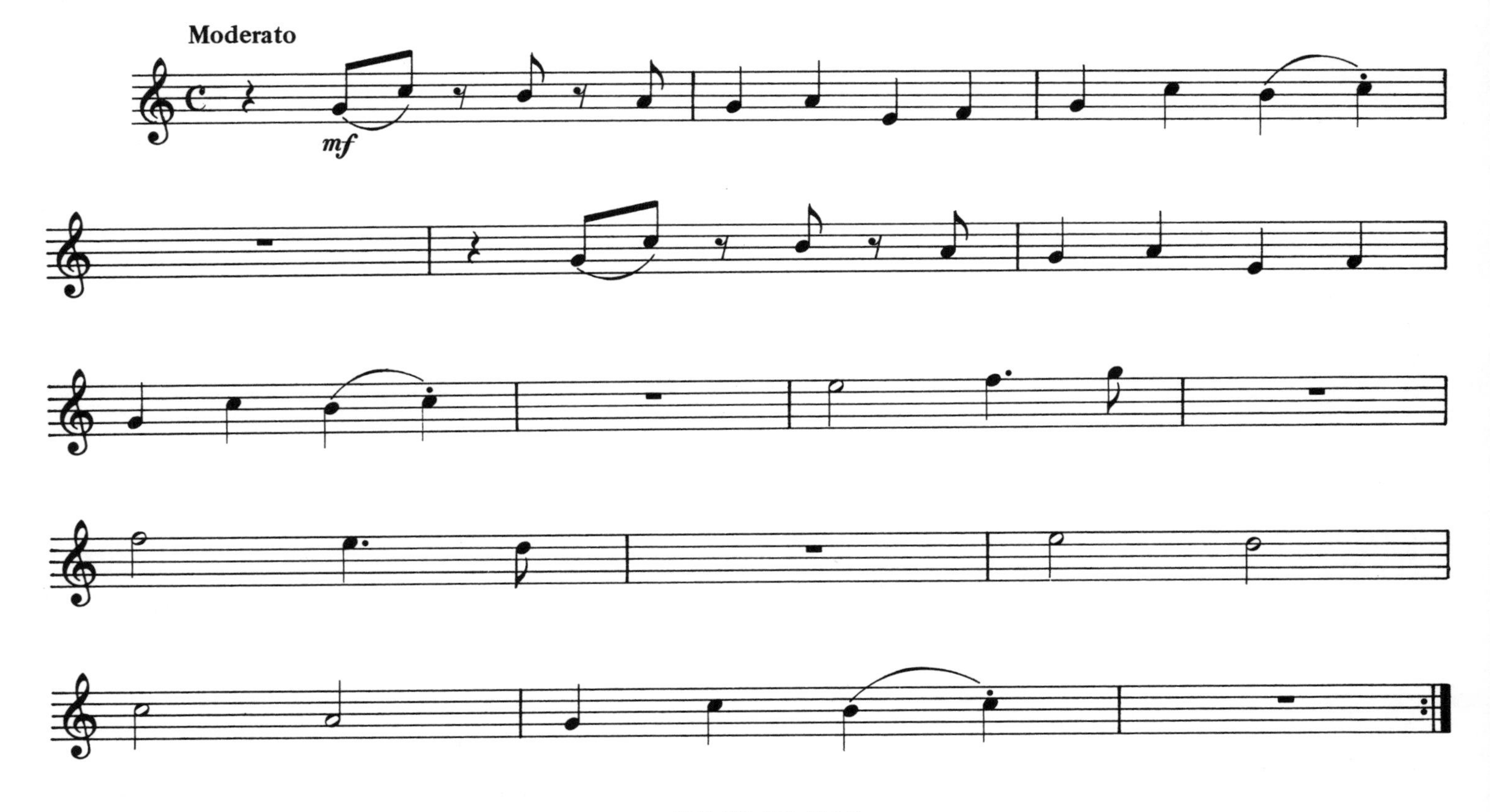

SUNNY

Words and Music: Bobby Hebb

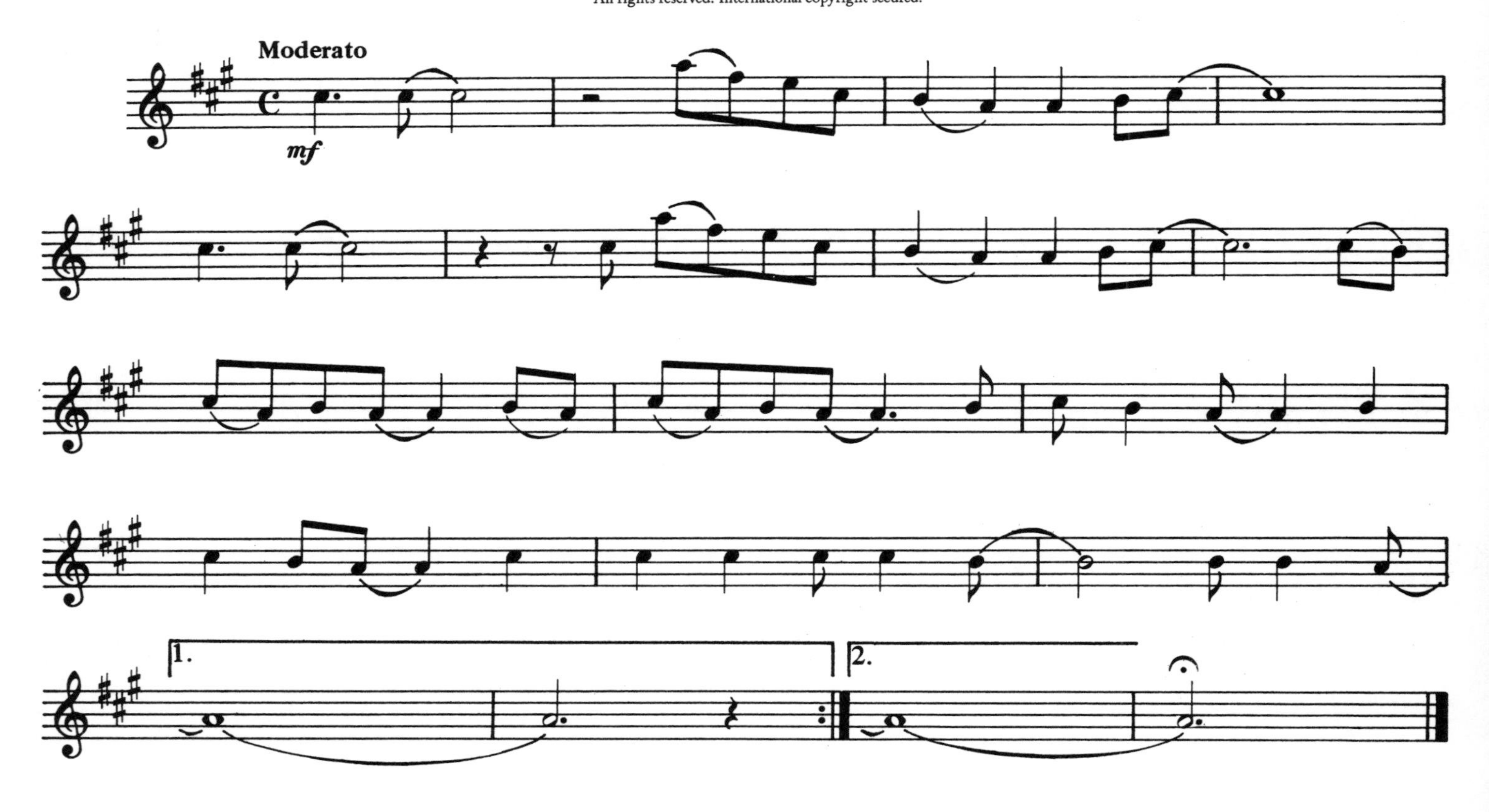

SWEET SUE—JUST YOU

Words: Will J. Harris
Music: Victor Young

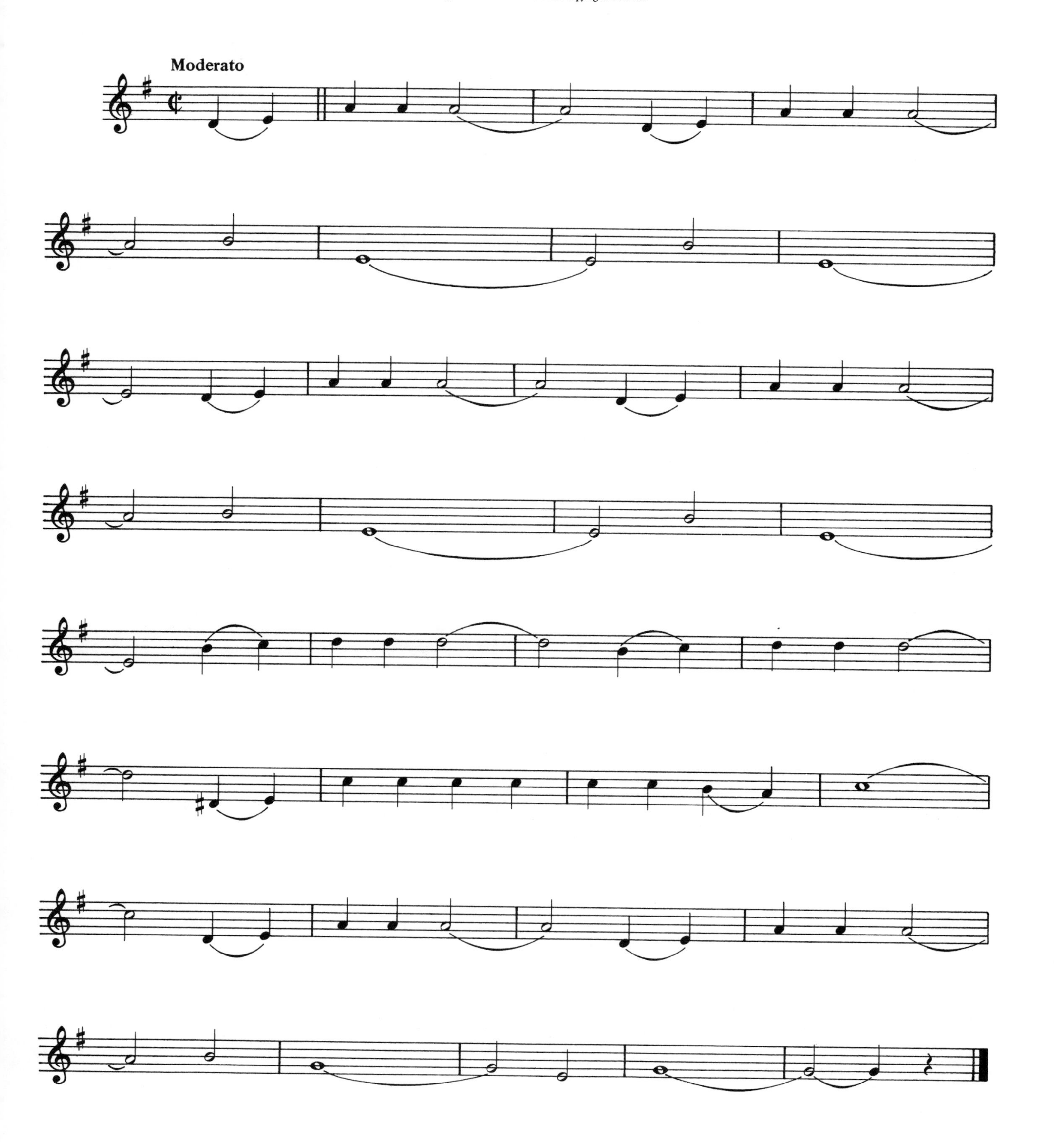

ROMANCE (from "Eine Kleine Nachtmusik")

Traditional

TAKE THE 'A' TRAIN

Words and Music: Billy Strayhorn

TELSTAR

By: Joe Meek

VIOLETS FOR YOUR FURS

Words: Tom Adair
Music: Matt Dennis

TIME ON MY HANDS

Words: Harold Adamson and Mack Gordon
Music: Vincent Youmans

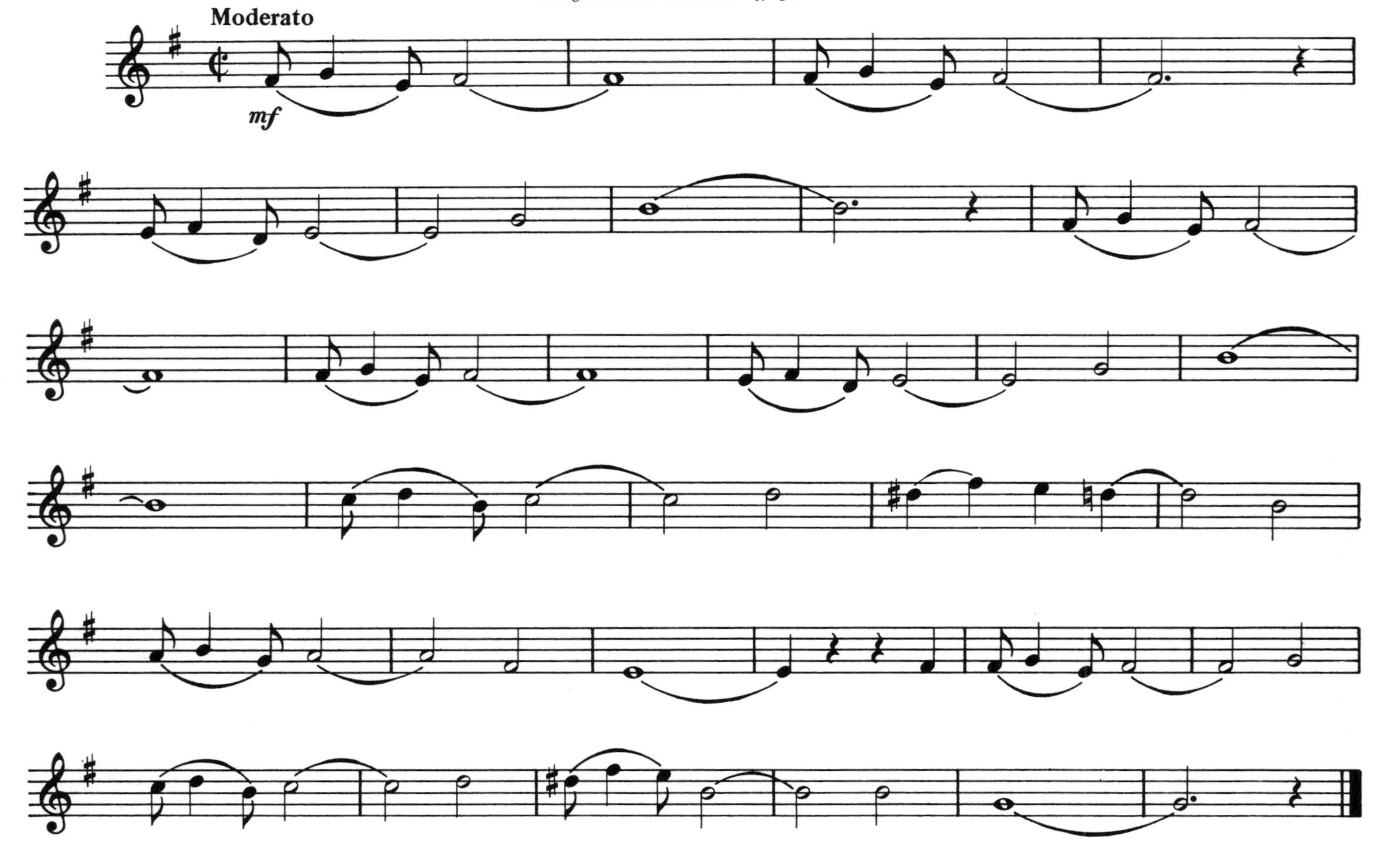

UNDECIDED

Words: Sid Robin
Music Charles Shavers

UNION OF THE SNAKE

Words and Music: Duran Duran

WALK DON'T RUN

By: Shorty Rogers

WALKING ON THE MOON

Words and Music: Sting

WALKIN' SHOES

By: Gerry Mulligan

THE WILD BOYS

Words and Music: Duran Duran

WAY DOWN YONDER IN NEW ORLEANS

Words and Music: Henry Creamer and Turner Layton

WE DON'T NEED ANOTHER HERO

Words and Music: Graham Lyle and Terry Britten

1.
2.
D. S. to fade on chorus

WOODCHOPPER'S BALL

By: Joe Bishop and Woody Herman

THE WORD GIRL

Words and Music: Green and David Gamson

ACROSS THE UNIVERSE

Words and Music: John Lennon and Paul McCartney

16000 8/93